BEST LOVED POEMS OF ALL TIME

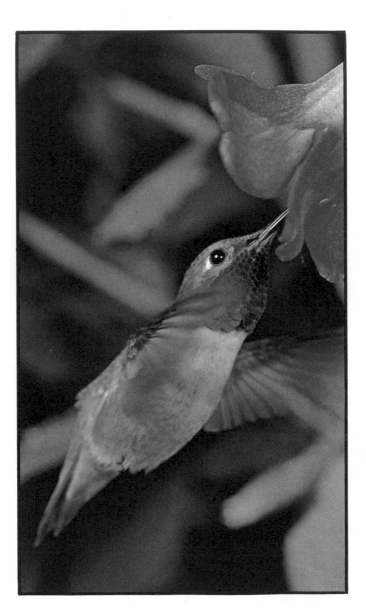

BEST LOVED POEMS OF ALL TIME

Selected by

Gail Harano

HALLMARK EDITIONS

TITLE INDEX

BEST LOVED POEMS

A SONG FROM SYLVAN
Louise Imogen Guiney

The little cares that fretted me,
I lost them yesterday
Among the fields above the sea,
Among the winds at play;
Among the lowing herds,
The rustling of the trees,
Among the singing birds,
The humming of the bees.

The fears of what may come to pass,
I cast them all away,
Among the clover-scented grass,
Among the new-mown hay;
Among the husking of the corn,
Where the drowsy poppies nod,
Where ill thoughts die
        and good are born,
Out in the fields with God.

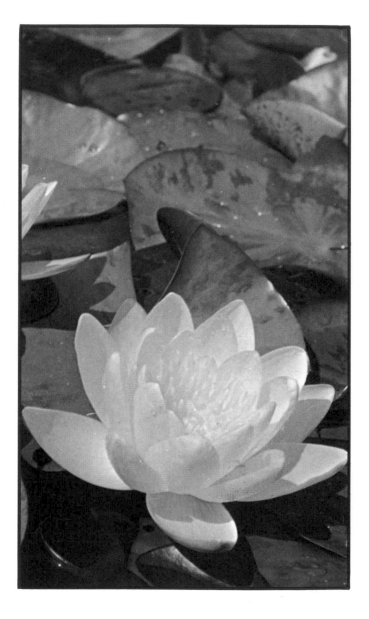

A THING OF BEAUTY
John Keats

A thing of beauty is a joy for ever:
Its loveliness increases; it will never
Pass into nothingness; but still will keep
A bower quiet for us, and a sleep
Full of sweet dreams, and health,
       and quiet breathing.
Therefore, on every morrow, are we wreathing
A flowery band to bind us to the earth,
Spite of despondence, of the inhuman dearth
Of noble natures, of the gloomy days,
Of all the unhealthy and o'er-darkened ways
Made for our searching: yes, in spite of all,
Some shape of beauty moves away the pall
From our dark spirits. Such the sun, the moon,
Trees old and young, sprouting a shady boon
For simple sheep; and such are daffodils
With the green world they live in; and clear rills
That for themselves a cooling covert make
'Gainst the hot season; the mid-forest brake,
Rich with a sprinkling of fair musk-rose blooms:
And such too is the grandeur of the dooms
We have imagined for the mighty dead;
                    All lovely

All lovely tales that we have heard or read:
An endless fountain of immortal drink,
Pouring unto us from the heaven's brink.
Nor do we merely feel these essences
For one short hour; no, even as the trees
That whisper round a temple become soon
Dear as the temple's self, so does the moon,
The passion poesy, glories infinite,
Haunt us till they become a cheering light
Unto our souls and bound to us so fast,
That, whether there be shine, or gloom o'ercast,
They always must be with us, or we die.

FROM ENDYMION

OUTWITTED
Edwin Markham

He drew a circle that shut me out—
Heretic, rebel, a thing to flout.
But Love and I had the wit to win:
We drew a circle that took him in!

SHE WALKS IN BEAUTY
George Gordon, Lord Byron

She walks in beauty, like the night
Of cloudless climes and starry skies;
And all that's best of dark and bright
Meet in her aspect and her eyes:
Thus mellowed to that tender light
Which heaven to gaudy day denies.

One shade the more, one ray the less,
Had half impaired the nameless grace
Which waves in every raven tress,
Or softly lightens o'er her face;
Where thoughts serenely sweet express
How pure, how dear, their dwelling-place.

And on that cheek, and o'er that brow,
So soft, so calm, yet eloquent,
The smiles that win, the tints that glow,
But tell of days in goodness spent,
A mind at peace with all below,
A heart whose love is innocent!

GROW OLD ALONG WITH ME
Robert Browning

Grow old along with me!
The best is yet to be,
The last of life, for which
   the first was made:
Our times are in his hand
Who saith, "A whole I planned,
Youth shows but half;
   trust God: see all, nor be afraid!"

FROM RABBI BEN EZRA

PIPPA'S SONG
Robert Browning

The year's at the spring,
And day's at the morn;
Morning's at seven;
The hillside's dew-pearl'd;
The lark's on the wing;
The snail's on the thorn;
God's in His heaven—
All's right with the world!

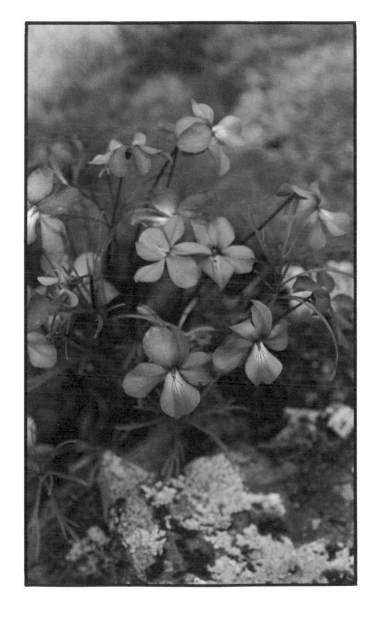

THE PASSIONATE SHEPHERD
TO HIS LOVE
Christopher Marlowe

Come live with me and be my love,
And we will all the pleasures prove
That valleys, groves, and hills, and fields,
Woods or steepy mountain yields.

And we will sit upon the rocks,
Seeing the shepherds feed their flocks
By shallow rivers, to whose falls
Melodious birds sing madrigals.

And I will make thee beds of roses,
And a thousand fragrant posies:
A cap of flowers, and a kirtle,
Embroider'd all with leaves of myrtle.

A gown made of the finest wool,
Which from our pretty lambs we'll pull;
Fair lined slippers for the cold,
With buckles of the purest gold.

A belt of straw and ivy buds,
With coral clasps and amber studs:
And if these pleasures may thee move,
Come live with me and be my love.

The shepherd swains shall dance and sing
For thy delight each May morning.
If these delights thy mind may move,
Come live with me and be my love.

THE RAINBOW
William Wordsworth

My heart leaps up when I behold
A Rainbow in the sky:
So was it when my life began;
So is it now I am a Man;
So be it when I shall grow old,
Or let me die!
The Child is Father of the Man;
And I could wish my days to be
Bound each to each by natural piety.

MINIVER CHEEVY
Edwin Arlington Robinson

Miniver Cheevy, child of scorn,
Grew lean while he assailed the seasons;
He wept that he was ever born,
And he had reasons.

Miniver loved the days of old
When swords were bright and steeds
       were prancing.
The vision of a warrior bold
Would set him dancing.

Miniver sighed for what was not,
And dreamed, and rested from his labors;
He dreamed of Thebes and Camelot,
And Priam's neighbors.

Miniver mourned the ripe renown
That made so many a name so fragrant;
He mourned Romance, now on the town,
And Art, a vagrant.

Miniver loved the Medici,
Albeit he had never seen one;
He would have sinned incessantly
Could he have been one.

Miniver cursed the commonplace
And eyed a khaki suit with loathing;
He missed the medieval grace
Of iron clothing.

Miniver scorned the gold he sought,
But sore annoyed was he without it;
Miniver thought, and thought, and thought,
And thought about it.

Miniver Cheevy, born too late,
Scratched his head and kept on thinking:
Miniver coughed, and called it fate,
And kept on drinking.

HOW DO I LOVE THEE?
Elizabeth Barret Browning

How do I love thee? Let me count the ways.
I love thee to the depth and breadth and height
My soul can reach, when feeling out of sight
For the ends of Being and ideal Grace.
I love thee to the level of every day's
Most quiet need, by sun and candle-light.
I love thee freely, as men strive for Right;
I love thee purely, as they turn from Praise.
I love thee with the passion put to use
In my old griefs, and with my childhood's faith.
I love thee with a love I seemed to lose
With my lost saints,—I love thee with the breath,
Smiles, tears, of all my life!—and, if God choose,
I shall but love thee better after death.

FROM SONNETS FROM THE PORTUGUESE

DEATH BE NOT PROUD
John Donne

Death be not proud, though some have called thee
Mighty and dreadful, for thou art not so,
For those whom thou thinkest thou dost overthrow
Die not, poor death, nor yet canst thou kill me.
From rest and sleep, which but thy picture be,
Much pleasure, then from thee,
      much more must flow,
And soonest our best men with thee do go,
Rest of their bones, and soul's delivery.
Thou art slave to Fate, Chance, kings,
      and desperate men,
And dost with poison, war, and sickness dwell,
And poppy, or charms, can make us sleep as well,
And better than thy stroke;
      why swellest thou then?
One short sleep past, we wake eternally,
And death shall be no more; death, thou shalt die.

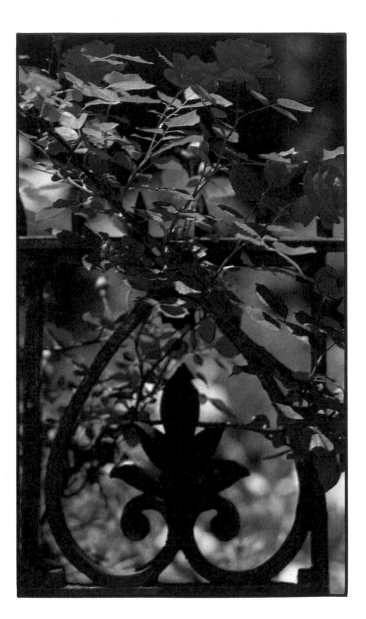

A RED, RED ROSE
Robert Burns

O, my luve is like a red, red rose,
That's newly sprung in June:
O, my luve is like the melodie
That's sweetly played in tune.

As fair art thou, my bonnie lass,
So deep in luve am I;
And I will luve thee still, my dear,
Till a' the seas gang dry.

Till a' the seas gang dry, my dear,
And the rocks melt wi' the sun;
And I will luve thee still, my dear,
While the sands o' life shall run.

And fare thee well, my only luve!
And fare thee well a while!
And I will come again, my luve,
Tho' it were ten thousand mile!

TO CELIA
Ben Jonson

Drink to me only with thine eyes,
      And I will pledge with mine;
Or leave a kiss but in the cup,
      And I'll not look for wine.
The thirst that from the soul doth rise
      Doth ask a drink divine;
But might I of Jove's nectar sup,
      I would not change for thine.

I sent thee late a rosy wreath,
      Not so much honoring thee
As giving it a hope that there
      It could not withered be:
But thou thereon didst only breathe
      And sent'st it back to me;
Since when it grows, and smells, I swear,
      Not of itself, but thee!

CROSSING THE BAR
Alfred, Lord Tennyson

Sunset and evening star,
      And one clear call for me,
And may there be no moaning of the bar,
      When I put out to sea.

But such a tide as moving seems asleep,
      . Too full for sound and foam,
When that which drew
      from out the boundless deep
      Turns again home.

Twilight and evening bell,
      And after that the dark!
And may there be no sadness of farewell,
      When I embark;

For tho' from out our bourne of time
      and place
      The flood may bear me far,
I hope to see my Pilot face to face
      When I have crossed the bar.

THE WORLD
IS TOO MUCH WITH US
William Wordsworth

The World is too much with us; late and soon,
Getting and spending, we lay waste our powers;
Little we see in Nature that is ours;
We have given our hearts away, a sordid boon!
The sea that bares her bosom to the moon;
The winds that will be howling at all hours,
And are up-gathered now like sleeping flowers;
For this, for everything, we are out of tune;
It moves us not.—Great God! I'd rather be
A Pagan suckled in a creed outworn,
So might I, standing on this pleasant lea,
Have glimpses that would make me less forlorn;
Have sight of Proteus rising from the sea,
Or hear old Triton blow his wreathed horn.

SHALL I COMPARE THEE
TO A SUMMER'S DAY?
William Shakespeare

Shall I compare thee to a summer's day?
Thou art more lovely and more temperate.
Rough winds do shake the darling buds of May,
And summer's lease hath all too short a date:
Sometime too hot the eye of heaven shines,
And often is his gold complexion dimm'd;
And every fair from fair some time declines,
By chance, or nature's changing course, untrimm'd;
But thy eternal summer shall not fade
Nor lose possession of that fair thou ow'st;
Nor shall Death brag thou wand'rest in his shade,
When in eternal lines to time thou grow'st.

   So long as men can breathe or eyes can see,
   So long lives this, and this gives life to thee.

THE BUILDERS
Henry Wadsworth Longfellow

All are architects of Fate,
       Working in these walls of Time;
Some with massive deeds and great,
       Some with ornaments of rhyme.

Nothing useless is, or low;
       Each thing in its place is best;
And what seems but idle show
       Strengthens and supports the rest.

For the structure that we raise,
       Time is with materials filled;
Our todays and yesterdays
       Are the blocks with which we build.

Truly shape and fashion these;
       Leave no yawning gaps between;
Think not, because no man sees,
       Such things will remain unseen.

In the elder days of Art,
       Builders wrought with greatest care
Each minute and unseen part;
       For the gods see everywhere.

Let us do our work as well.
Both the unseen and the seen;
Make the house where gods may dwell
Beautiful, entire, and clean.

Else our lives are incomplete,
Standing in these walls of Time,
Broken stairways, where the feet
Stumble, as they seek to climb.

Build today, then, strong and sure,
With a firm and ample base;
And ascending and secure
Shall tomorrow find its place.

Thus alone can we attain
To those turrets, where the eye
Sees the world as one vast plain,
And one boundless reach of sky.

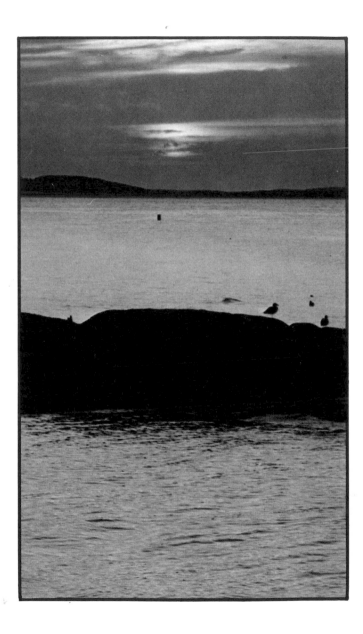

SEA FEVER
John Masefield

I must go down to the seas again,
       to the lonely sea and the sky,
And all I ask is a tall ship
       and a star to steer her by;
And the wheel's kick and the wind's song
       and the white sail's shaking,
And a grey mist on the sea's face,
       and a grey dawn breaking.

I must go down to the seas again,
       for the call of the running tide
Is a wild call and a clear call
       that may not be denied;
And all I ask is a windy day
       with the white clouds flying,
And the flung spray and the blown spume,
       and the sea-gulls crying.

                                  I must

I must go down to the seas again,
      to the vagrant gypsy life,
To the gull's way and the whale's way,
      where the wind's like a whetted knife;
And all I ask is a merry yarn
      from a laughing fellow-rover,
And quiet sleep and sweet dream
      when the long trick's over.

JENNY KISS'D ME
Leigh Hunt

Jenny kiss'd me when we met,
      Jumping from the chair she sat in;
Time, you thief, who love to get
      Sweets into your list, put that in!
Say I'm weary, say I'm sad,
      Say that health
      and wealth have miss'd me,
Say I'm growing old, but add,
      Jenny kiss'd me.

TO THE VIRGINS,
TO MAKE MUCH OF TIME
Robert Herrick

Gather ye rosebuds while ye may,
Old Time is still a-flying;
And this same flower that smiles today,
Tomorrow will be dying.

The glorious lamp of heaven, the sun,
The higher he's a-getting,
The sooner will his race be run,
And nearer he's to setting.

That age is best which is the first,
When youth and blood are warmer;
But being spent, the worse and worst
Times still succeed the former.

Then be not coy, but use your time,
And while ye may, go marry;
For, having lost but once your prime,
You may forever tarry.

JUNE
James Russell Lowell

And what is so rare as a day in June?
Then, if ever, come perfect days;
Then Heaven tries earth if it be in tune,
And over it softly her warm ear lays;
Whether we look, or whether we listen,
We hear life murmur, or see it glisten;
Every clod feels a stir of might,
An instinct within it that reaches and towers,
And, groping blindly above it for light,
Climbs to a soul in grass and flowers;
The flush of life may well be seen
Thrilling back over hills and valleys;
The cowslip startles in meadows green,
The buttercup catches the sun in its chalice,
And there's never a leaf nor a blade too mean
To be some happy creature's palace;
The little bird sits at his door in the sun,
Atilt like a blossom among the leaves,
And lets his illumined being o'errun
With the deluge of summer it receives;
His mate feels the eggs beneath her wings,
And the heart in her dumb breast
       flutters and sings;
                    He sings

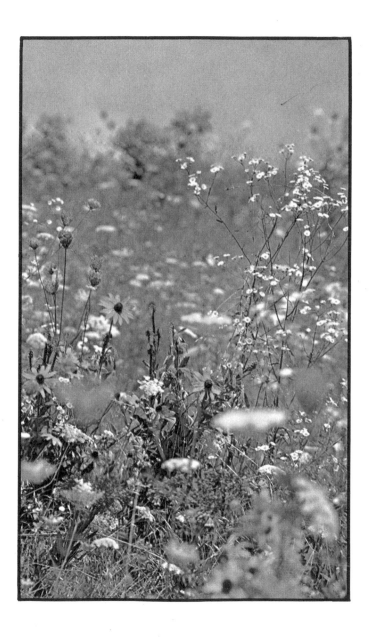

He sings to the wide world and she to her nest—
In the nice ear of Nature, which song is the best?
Now is the high-tide of the year,
And whatever of life hath ebbed away
Comes flooding back with a ripply cheer,
Into every bare inlet and creek and bay;
Now the heart is so full that a drop overfills it,
We are happy now because God wills it;
No matter how barren the past may have been,
'Tis enough for us now that the leaves are green;
We sit in the warm shade and feel right well
How the sap creeps up and the blossoms swell;
We may shut our eyes,
       but we cannot help knowing
That skies are clear and grass is growing;
The breeze comes whispering in our ear,
That dandelions are blossoming near,
That maize has sprouted, that streams are flowing,
That the river is bluer than the sky,
That the robin is plastering his house hard by;
And if the breeze kept the good news back,
For other couriers we should not lack;
We could guess it all by yon heifer's lowing,—
And hark! how clear bold chanticleer,
Warmed with the new wine of the year,
Tells all in his lusty crowing!

FROM THE VISION OF SIR LAUNFAL

I NEVER SAW A MOOR
Emily Dickinson

I never saw a Moor—
I never saw the Sea—
Yet know I how the Heather looks
And what a Billow be.

I never spoke with God
Nor visited in Heaven—
Yet certain am I of the spot
As if the Checks were given—

NOT IN VAIN
Emily Dickinson

If I can stop one heart from breaking,
I shall not live in vain:
If I can ease one life the aching,
Or cool one pain,
Or help one fainting robin
Unto his nest again,
I shall not live in vain.

NON SUM QUALIS ERAM BONAE
SUB REGNO CYNARAE
Ernest Dowson

Last night, ah, yesternight, betwixt her lips and mine
There fell thy shadow, Cynara! Thy breath was shed
Upon my soul between the kisses and the wine;
And I was desolate and sick of an old passion—
Yea, I was desolate and bowed my head.
I have been faithful to thee, Cynara!—in my fashion.

All night upon mine heart I felt her warm heart beat,
Night-long within mine arms in love and sleep she lay;
Surely the kisses of her bought red mouth were sweet;
But I was desolate and sick of an old passion,
When I woke and found the dawn was gray:
I have been faithful to thee, Cynara!—in my fashion.

I have forgot much, Cynara! Gone with the wind,
Flung roses, roses riotously with the throng.
Dancing, to put thy pale, lost lilies out of mind;
But I was desolate and sick of an old passion—
Yea, all the time, because the dance was long:
I have been faithful to thee, Cynara!—in my fashion.

I cried for madder music and for stronger wine,
But when the feast is finished and the lamps expire,
Then falls thy shadow, Cynara! The night is thine;
And I am desolate and sick of an old passion,
Yea, hungry for the lips of my desire:
I have been faithful to thee, Cynara!—in my fashion.

OZYMANDIAS
Percy Bysshe Shelley

I met a traveller from an antique land
Who said: Two vast and trunkless legs of stone
Stand in the desert . . . Near them, on the sand,
Half sunk, a shattered visage lies, whose frown,
And wrinkled lip, and sneer of cold command,
Tell that its sculptor well those passions read
Which yet survive, stamped on these lifeless things,
The hand that mocked them, and the heart that fed.
And on the pedestal these words appear:
'My name is Ozymandias, king of kings:
Look on my works, ye Mighty, and despair!'
Nothing beside remains. Round the decay
Of that colossal wreck, boundless and bare
The lone and level sands stretch far away.

THE BAREFOOT BOY
John Greenleaf Whittier

Blessings on thee, little man,
Barefoot boy, with cheek of tan!
With thy turned-up pantaloons,
And thy merry whistled tunes;
With thy red lip, redder still,
Kissed by strawberries on the hill;
With the sunshine on thy face,
Through thy torn brim's jaunty grace,
From my heart I give thee joy,—
I was once a barefoot boy.
Prince thou art,—the grown-up man
Only is republican,
Let the million-dollared ride!
Barefoot, trudging at his side,
Thou hast more than he can buy,
In the reach of ear and eye—
Outward sunshine, inward joy;
Blessings on thee, barefoot boy!

Oh, for boyhood's painless play,
Sleep that wakes in laughing day,
Health that mocks the doctor's rules,
Knowledge never learned of schools,
Of the wild bee's morning chase,
Of the wild flower's time and place,
Flight of fowl and habitude
Of the tenants of the wood;
How the tortoise bears his shell,
How the woodchuck digs his cell,
And the groundmole sinks his well;
How the robin feeds her young,
How the oriole's nest is hung,
Where the whitest lilies blow,
Where the freshest berries grow,
Where the ground-nut trails its vine,
Where the wood-grape's clusters shine,
Of the black wasp's cunning way,—
Mason of his walls of clay,—
And the architectural plans
Of gray-hornet artisans!—
For, eschewing books and tasks,
Nature answers all he asks,
Hand in hand with her he walks,
Face to face with her he talks,
Part and parcel of her joy,—
Blessings on the barefoot boy!

From ELEGY WRITTEN
IN A COUNTRY CHURCHYARD
Thomas Gray

The curfew tolls the knell of parting day,
The lowing herd winds slowly o'er the lea,
The plowman homeward plods his weary way,
And leaves the world to darkness and to me. . . .

Beneath those rugged elms, that yew-tree's shade,
Where heaves the turf in many a mould'ring heap,
Each in his narrow cell for ever laid,
The rude Forefathers of the hamlet sleep. . . .

For them no more the blazing hearth shall burn,
Or busy housewife ply her evening care:
No children run to lisp their sire's return,
Or climb his knees the envied kiss to share. . . .

Let not Ambition mock their useful toil,
Their homely joys, and destiny obscure;
Nor Grandeur hear with a disdainful smile
The short and simple annals of the poor.

The boast

The boast of heraldry, the pomp of pow'r,
And all that beauty, all that wealth e'er gave,
Awaits alike th' inevitable hour:
The paths of glory lead but to the grave. . . .

Perhaps in this neglected spot is laid
Some heart once pregnant with celestial fire;
Hands, that the rod of empire might have sway'd,
Or waked to ecstasy the living lyre.

But Knowledge to their eyes her ample page
Rich with the spoils of time did ne'er unroll;
Chill Penury repress'd their noble rage,
And froze the genial current of the soul.

Full many a gem of purest ray serene
The dark unfathom'd caves of ocean bear:
Full many a flower is born to blush unseen,
And waste its sweetness on the desert air. . . .

Far from the madding crowd's ignoble strife
Their sober wishes never learn'd to stray;
Along the cool sequester'd vale of life
They kept the noiseless tenor of their way. . . .

IN FLANDERS FIELDS
John McCrae

In Flanders fields the poppies blow
Between the crosses, row on row,
That mark our place; and in the sky
The larks, still bravely singing, fly
Scarce heard amid the guns below.

We are the Dead. Short days ago
We lived, felt dawn, saw sunset glow,
Loved and were loved, and now we lie
In Flanders fields.

Take up our quarrel with the foe:
To you from failing hands we throw
The torch; be yours to hold it high.
If ye break faith with us who die
We shall not sleep, though poppies grow
In Flanders fields.

THE TIGER
William Blake

Tiger! Tiger! burning bright,
In the forests of the night:
What immortal hand or eye
Could frame thy fearful symmetry?

In what distant deeps or skies
Burnt the fire of thine eyes?
On what wings dare he aspire?
What the hand dare seize the fire?

And what shoulder, and what art,
Could twist the sinews of thy heart?
And when thy heart began to beat,
What dread hand? and what dread feet?

What the hammer? what the chain?
In what furnace was thy brain?
What the anvil? what dread grasp
Dare its deadly terrors clasp?

When the stars threw down their spears
And watered heaven with their tears:
Did he smile his work to see?
Did he who made the Lamb make thee?

Tiger! Tiger! burning bright,
In the forests of the night:
What immortal hand or eye,
Dare frame thy fearful symmetry?

DUST OF SNOW
Robert Frost

The way a crow
Shook down on me
The dust of snow
From a hemlock tree

Has given my heart
A change of mood
And saved some part
Of a day I had rued.

From THE HOUSE
BY THE SIDE OF THE ROAD
Sam Walter Foss

*'He was a friend to man, and lived
in a house by the side of the road.'*–HOMER

There are hermit souls that live withdrawn
In the peace of their self-content;
There are souls, like stars, that dwell apart,
In a fellowless firmament;
There are pioneer souls that blaze their paths
Where highways never ran;
But let me live by the side of the road
And be a friend to man.

Let me live in a house by the side of the road,
Where the race of men go by—
The men who are good
         and the men who are bad,
As good and as bad as I.
I would not sit in the scorner's seat,
Or hurl the cynic's ban;
Let me live in a house by the side of the road
And be a friend to man. . . .

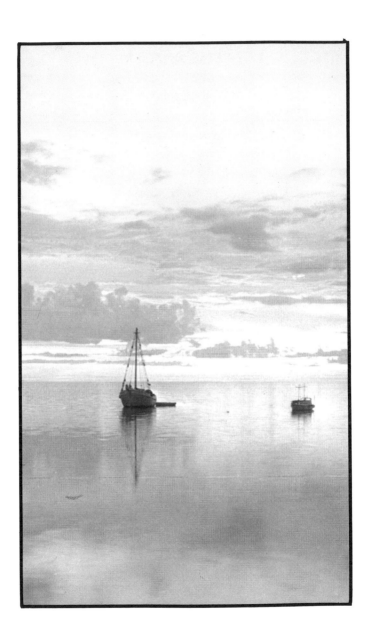

WHEN I CONSIDER
HOW MY LIGHT IS SPENT
John Milton

When I consider how my light is spent
Ere half my days in this dark world and wide,
And that one talent which is death to hide
Lodged with me useless, though my soul more bent
To serve therewith my Maker, and present
My true account, lest he returning chide,
"Doth God exact day-labor, light denied?"
I fondly ask. But Patience, to prevent
That murmur, soon replies, "God doth not need
Either man's work or his own gifts. Who best
Bear his mild yoke, they serve him best. His state
Is kingly: thousands at his bidding speed,
And post o'er land and ocean without rest;
They also serve who only stand and wait."

O CAPTAIN! MY CAPTAIN!
Walt Whitman

O Captain! my Captain! our fearful trip is done;
The ship has weather'd every rack,
     the prize we sought is won;
The port is near, the bells I hear,
     the people all exulting,
While follow eyes the steady keel,
     the vessel grim and daring:
     But O heart! heart! heart!
     O the bleeding drops of red,
     Where on the deck my Captain lies,
     Fallen cold and dead.

O Captain! my Captain! rise up and hear the bells;
Rise up—for you the flag is flung—
     for you the bugle trills;
For you bouquets and ribbon'd wreaths—
     for you the shores a-crowding;
For you they call, the swaying mass,
     their eager faces turning:
     Here Captain! dear father!
     This arm beneath your head;
     It is some dream that on the deck
     You've fallen cold and dead.

My Captain

My Captain does not answer,
   his lips are pale and still;
My father does not feel my arm,
   he has no pulse or will;
The ship is anchor'd safe and sound,
   its voyage closed and done;
From fearful trip the victor ship
   comes in with object won:
   Exult, O shores, and ring, O bells!
   But I, with mournful tread,
   Walk the deck my Captain lies,
   Fallen cold and dead.

FOG
Carl Sandburg

The fog comes
on little cat feet.

It sits looking
over harbor and city
on silent haunches
and then, moves on.

WHEN I WAS ONE-AND-TWENTY
A. E. *Housman*

When I was one-and-twenty
  I heard a wise man say,
"Give crowns and pounds and guineas
  But not your heart away;
Give pearls away and rubies
  But keep your fancy free."
But I was one-and-twenty,
  No use to talk to me.

When I was one-and-twenty
  I heard him say again,
"The heart out of the bosom
  Was never given in vain;
'Tis paid with sighs a plenty
  And sold for endless rue."
And I am two-and-twenty,
  And oh, 'tis true, 'tis true.

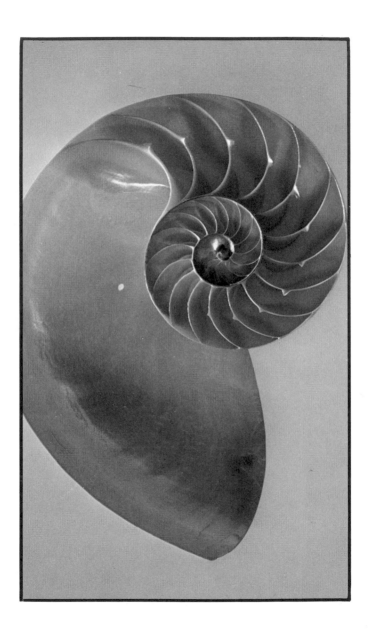

THE CHAMBERED NAUTILUS
Oliver Wendell Holmes

This is the ship of pearl which, poets feign,
      Sails the unshadowed main,—
      The venturous bark that flings
On the sweet summer wind its purpled wings
In gulfs enchanted, where the Siren sings,
      And coral reefs lie bare,
Where the cold sea-maids rise
      to sun their streaming hair.

Its webs of living gauze no more unfurl;
      Wrecked is the ship of pearl!
      And every chambered cell,
Where its dim dreaming life was wont to dwell,
As the frail tenant shaped his growing shell,
      Before thee lies revealed,—
Its irised ceiling rent, its sunless crypt unsealed!

Year after year beheld the silent toil
      That spread his lustrous coil;
      Still, as the spiral grew,
He left the past year's dwelling for the new,
Stole with soft step its shining archway through,
      Built up its idle door,
                  Stretched in

Stretched in his last-found home,
        and knew the old no more.

Thanks for the heavenly message brought by thee,
        Child of the wandering sea,
        Cast from her lap, forlorn!
From thy dead lips a clearer note is born
Than ever Triton blew from wreathed horn!
        While on mine ear it rings,
Through the deep caves of thought
        I hear a voice that sings:

Build thee more stately mansions, O my soul,
        As the swift seasons roll!
        Leave thy low-vaulted past!
Let each new temple, nobler than the last,
Shut thee from heaven with a dome more vast,
        Till thou at length art free,
Leaving thine outgrown shell
        by life's unresting sea!

CONCORD HYMN
Ralph Waldo Emerson

By the rude bridge that arched the flood,
Their flag to April's breeze unfurled,
Here once the embattled farmers stood,
And fired the shot heard round the world.

The foe long since in silence slept;
Alike the conqueror silent sleeps;
And Time the ruined bridge has swept
Down the dark stream which seaward creeps.

On this green bank, by this soft stream,
We set today a votive stone;
That memory may their deed redeem,
When, like our sires, our sons are gone.

Spirit, that made those heroes dare
To die, and leave their children free,
Bid Time and Nature gently spare
The shaft we raise to them and thee.

DOVER BEACH
Matthew Arnold

The sea is calm to-night.
The tide is full, the moon lies fair
Upon the straits;—on the French coast the light
Gleams and is gone; the cliffs of England stand,
Glimmering and vast, out in the tranquil bay.
Come to the window, sweet is the night-air!
Only, from the long line of spray
Where the sea meets the moon-blanched land,
Listen! you hear the grating roar
Of pebbles which the waves draw back, and fling,
At their return, up the high strand,
Begin, and cease, and then again begin,
With tremulous cadence slow, and bring
The eternal note of sadness in.

Sophocles long ago
Heard it on the Ægean, and it brought
Into his mind the turbid ebb and flow
Of human misery; we
Find also in the sound a thought,
Hearing it by this distant northern sea.

The sea of faith
Was once, too, at the full, the round earth's shore
Lay like the folds of a bright girdle furled.
But now I only hear
Its melancholy, long, withdrawing roar,
Retreating, to the breath
Of the night-wind, down the vast edges drear
And naked shingles of the world.

Ah, love, let us be true
To one another! for the world, which seems
To lie before us like a land of dreams,
So various, so beautiful, so new,
Hath really neither joy, nor love, nor light,
Nor certitude, nor peace, nor help for pain;
And we are here as on a darkling plain
Swept with confused alarms
        of struggle and flight,
Where ignorant armies clash by night.

ANNABEL LEE
Edgar Allen Poe

It was many and many a year ago,
      In a kingdom by the sea,
That a maiden there lived whom you may know
      By the name of Annabel Lee;–
And this maiden she lived with no other thought
      Than to love and be loved by me.

I was a child and *she* was a child,
      In this kingdom by the sea,
But we loved with a love that was more than love–
      I and my Annabel Lee–
With a love that the winged seraphs in Heaven
      Coveted her and me.

And this was the reason that, long ago,
      In this kingdom by the sea,
A wind blew out of a cloud, chilling
      My beautiful Annabel Lee;
So that her high-born kinsmen came
      And bore her away from me,
To shut her up in a sepulcher
      In this kingdom by the sea.

The angels, not half so happy in Heaven,
       Went envying her and me:—
Yes!—that was the reason (as all men know,
       In this kingdom by the sea)
That the wind came out of the cloud, by night,
       Chilling and killing my Annabel Lee.

But our love it was stronger by far than the love
       Of those who were older than we—
       Of many far wiser than we—
And neither the angels in Heaven above,
       Nor the demons down under the sea,
Can ever dissever my soul from the soul
       Of the beautiful Annabel Lee:—

For the moon never beams
       without bringing me dreams
       Of the beautiful Annabel Lee;
And the stars never rise but I feel the bright eyes
       Of the beautiful Annabel Lee;
And so, all the night-tide, I lie down by the side
Of my darling,—my darling,—my life and my bride,
       In her sepulcher there by the sea—
       In her tomb by the sounding sea.

IF
Rudyard Kipling

If you can keep your head when all about you
       Are losing theirs and blaming it on you;
If you can trust yourself when all men doubt you,
       But make allowance for their doubting too:
If you can wait and not be tired by waiting,
       Or, being lied about, don't deal in lies,
Or being hated don't give way to hating,
       And yet don't look too good,
       nor talk too wise;

If you can dream—and not make dreams your master;
       If you can think—
       and not make thoughts your aim,
If you can meet with Triumph and Disaster
       And treat those two impostors just the same:
If you can bear to hear the truth you've spoken
       Twisted by knaves to make a trap for fools,
Or watch the things you gave your life to, broken,
       And stoop and build 'em up
       with worn-out tools;

If you can make one heap of all your winnings
       And risk it on one turn of pitch-and-toss,
And lose, and start again at your beginnings,
       And never breathe a word about your loss:
If you can force your heart and nerve and sinew
       To serve your turn long after they are gone,
And so hold on when there is nothing in you
       Except the Will which says to them: "Hold on!"

If you can talk with crowds and keep your virtue,
       Or walk with Kings—
       nor lose the common touch,
If neither foes nor loving friends can hurt you,
       If all men count with you, but none too much:
If you can fill the unforgiving minute
       With sixty seconds' worth of distance run,
Yours is the Earth and everything that's in it,
       And—which is more—you'll be a Man, my son!

Set in Cartier roman and italic, a modern serif
designed by the Canadian typographer Carl Dair
in honor of Canada's centenary of confederation.
Printed on Hallmark Eggshell Book paper.
Designed by J. William Burdett.
The designer gratefully acknowledges
the assistance of Richard Fanolio
in compiling the photographs in this edition.